D1263824

Engineering Applications of Fluid Mechanics

Engineering Applications of Fluid Mechanics

By J. C. HUNSAKER

Department of Aeronautical Engineering
Massachusetts Institute of Technology

and B. G. RIGHTMIRE

Department of Mechanical Engineering
Massachusetts Institute of Technology

McGRAW-HILL BOOK COMPANY, INC.

NEW YORK AND LONDON

1947

ENGINEERING APPLICATIONS OF FLUID MECHANICS

COPYRIGHT, 1947, BY THE
McGRAW-HILL BOOK COMPANY, INC.

PRINTED IN THE UNITED STATES OF AMERICA

*All rights reserved. This book, or
parts thereof, may not be reproduced
in any form without permission of
the publishers.*

VIII

PREFACE

This book has grown out of some 12 years' experience with a course in fluid mechanics for an undergraduate class in the mechanical engineering department of the Massachusetts Institute of Technology.

The controlling importance of flow phenomena in nearly every type of machine and process led to the conversion of a traditional course in hydraulics into a more fundamental treatment of the action of fluids generally. The authors were more anxious that the student understand flow phenomena than that he be familiar with details of many practical devices. They attempted to give unity to the subject by the careful development, at an adult level, of the mechanics of fluids and to provide interest and utility by condensed treatment of selected types of engineering application.

The course is essentially an introduction to a field of engineering science that includes important subjects for later professional study. An introductory course should lay an adequate foundation for advanced work and should, therefore, deal both with mathematical reasoning and with experimental results. Recent advances in the efficiency of machines and engines have resulted from a better understanding of their operation. This understanding requires not so much the determination of over-all performance in terms of a few pressure and temperature measurements as a detailed exploration of flow conditions.

In such investigations fluid mechanics is of first importance, both in machines actually handling fluid, such as compressors and turbines, and also in engines, where controlled flow of air, fuel, and combustion gases is essential.

The application of Newton's laws of mechanics to fluids with the aid of the tools of mathematics gives an exact description of flow phenomena for certain idealized cases but only an approximate description for many practical cases. The greatest difficulty comes in real fluids from the effect of friction and the resulting turbulence and separation from the boundary surfaces designed to guide the flow. When the type of flow is too confused to be postulated with any confidence, mathematical analysis from first principles is usually hopeless.

First the naval architect and later the aeronautical engineer have been brilliantly successful in the use of models to solve such complicated problems. For this, a theory of similitude is necessary to ensure that the model experiments shall predict full-scale performance under the desired conditions. In view of the increasing importance of controlled experiments in mechanical engineering, in this text the authors have gone into the theory of dimensions and physical similitude with some care. They believe that the student is entitled to a full explanation of the apparently simple rules for conducting model experiments.

The theoretical behavior of an ideal frictionless fluid has been discussed in order to introduce the student to basic concepts governing pressure and velocity distribution. While no real fluid is frictionless, in many engineering problems friction in the main flow may be neglected. At the same time, friction can be the controlling factor near solid boundaries, as Prandtl showed in his theory of the boundary layer. The student is expected to appreciate the simplicity and elegance of the mathematical treatment of the ideal fluid and also the validity and logic of the simplifying assumptions on which the treatment of frictional flow is based. For these reasons, the authors have given more weight to hydro-mechanics and boundary-layer theory than might be expected in an introductory text.

An explanation should perhaps be made of what may appear in the early chapters to be an overelaborate analysis of self-evident phenomena, such as the conditions of static equilibrium. A mathematical formulation of very simple physical relations is developed with some care to ensure familiarity with certain powerful methods of analysis needed later. For example, the device of a potential function is introduced as the potential energy of a gravity field, in anticipation of the later use of a velocity potential to describe a velocity field. Teaching experience indicates that the calculus needs restatement when applied to physical quantities.

The material in Chaps. I to VIII is essentially that presented during the first term of a two-term course in fluid mechanics. Parts of the remaining chapters are covered in the second term, with emphasis on topics in Chaps. X, XI, XII, XIV, XV, and XVII. The students for whom this material is intended have had 2 years of physics and mathematics, including differential equations, and 1 year of applied mechanics.

Since the student is taking a parallel course in thermodynamics at the same time, certain topics that might logically be included have been omitted. Furthermore, the class is also engaged in a sequence of laboratory exercises involving instrumentation, fluid measurements, and determination of the operating characteristics of many examples of machinery. While this book is designed to illuminate such laboratory work, it is in no sense a laboratory manual nor is it descriptive of current practice.

The treatment of servomechanisms is included for use in a separate one-term elective course.

Acknowledgment is made of valuable help from those who have given the course, notably R. von Mises, C. B. Millikan, and H. Peters. The chapters on lubrication were largely written by J. T. Burwell. M. Rauscher helped with the material on jets, and C. E. Grosser with that on hydraulic transmissions. The authors, however, are responsible for the end product.

J. C. HUNSAKER

B. G. RIGHTMIRE

CAMBRIDGE, MASS.
October, 1947

CONTENTS

CHAPTER I

INTRODUCTORY SURVEY

1.1. Definition. Fluid mechanics is the special branch of general mechanics that applies its fundamental principles to fluids. These principles are Newton's laws of motion, the conservation of energy, and the indestructibility of matter. Fluid mechanics can describe and predict the behavior of fluids to the extent that we know their physical properties and to the extent that practicable methods of applied mathematics can be found.

1.2. Objective. The primary objective of fluid mechanics for a mechanical engineer is twofold, (1) to explain the facts of experience by the deduction of general rules and (2) to apply such general rules to predict, at least to a practical approximation, the fluid phenomena involved in the performance of ships, airplanes, engines, compressors, turbines, pipe lines, and wherever a working fluid is involved in the operation of machinery. The rules of fluid mechanics are also fundamental to lubrication, convectional heat transfer, ballistics, oceanography, and meteorology, where important modern developments have taken place as a result of analysis of observed facts. In nearly all actual cases, some simplifying assumptions must be made as to the physical properties of the fluid or as to the character of the flow.

1.3. Fluids and Solids. The word "fluid" (from Latin *fluidus*) means a substance having particles that readily change their relative positions. Fluid refers, therefore, to both gases and liquids, as opposed to solids.

Solids and fluids behave differently under the action of an applied force. The force necessary to produce deformation of a solid depends mainly on the amount of the deformation, as, for example, in the case of a spring. The force must be maintained in order to hold the deformation. In the case of a fluid the force depends primarily on the speed with which a deformation is produced. Such force tends to vanish when the speed of deformation approaches zero. The increased resistance accompanying any increase in the speed of a solid body moving through a fluid illustrates this characteristic.

1.4. Viscosity. A fluid has the property of resisting deformation in proportion to the rate of deformation. Experiment shows that in a flooded journal bearing in which the shaft and bearing are concentric the following proportionality holds:

$$\frac{F}{2\pi aL} \sim \frac{V}{h}$$

where F is the tangential force acting on the lubricant at the surface of the shaft and the other quantities are shown in Fig. 1.1. Since it is known that a fluid does not slip at a boundary, the ratio V/h measures the rate of deformation of the oil in the bearing. The ratio $F/2\pi aL$ is the shear force

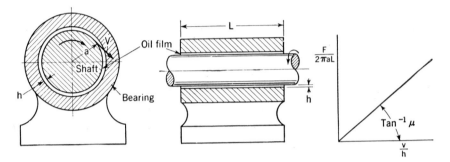

FIG. 1.1. — Oil viscosity causes shearing stress on the shaft of a flooded journal bearing.

per unit area, or shear stress exerted on the oil. The factor of proportionality between shear stress and rate of deformation is a property of the lubricating fluid and is called the "coefficient of viscosity" or, simply, "viscosity." The defining equation for viscosity of the lubricant in the journal bearing of Fig. 1.1 is

$$\text{Shear stress} = \frac{F}{2\pi aL} = \mu\frac{V}{h} \tag{1.1}$$

where μ is the viscosity. It is seen that the shear stress persists as long as the ratio V/h is greater than zero.

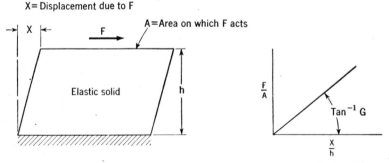

FIG. 1.2. — Shearing stress is proportional to deformation of an elastic solid.

Many substances, like metals, become true fluids when heated, while quasi solids, like jelly, pitch, and grease, may behave like fluids of very high viscosity.

For an elastic solid deformed by a shear force F the following equation holds:

$$\text{Shear stress} = \frac{F}{A} = G\frac{x}{h} \tag{1.2}$$

where G is a property of the solid called the "shear modulus" and the other quantities are shown in Fig. 1.2. The analogy between Eqs. (1.1) and (1.2) is obvious.

1.5. Plasticity. Metals heated just short of the melting point or strained beyond the elastic limit no longer behave as elastic solids but deform continuously under a constant load. This phenomenon of creep is characteristic of the plastic state of many solids. A metal in the plastic state is still polycrystalline and is not a fluid until melted. Hot metal in the rolling mill is plastic; so is cold metal under the very great local forces involved in wire drawing, press-forming, or cold-riveting. A yielding material that does not resist shear in proportion to the rate of shear is sometimes called a "non-Newtonian liquid." Heavy grease at low temperatures may exhibit a definite yield point and act like a plastic rather than like a true liquid.

The methods of fluid mechanics are ordinarily inapplicable to substances in the plastic state.

1.6. Perfect Fluid. Since real substances may partake of the fluid state to various degrees depending on conditions of temperature and pressure, application of the principles of fluid mechanics can be greatly simplified if the analysis is first made for an imaginary perfect fluid that is nonviscous, *i.e.*, for one that is subject to no shearing stress during motion. The assumption of such a frictionless fluid, under many circumstances, leads to very fair approximations to the behavior of real fluids of low viscosity, such as, for example, air, water, and alcohol.

It should be noted that in problems of statics, since there is no motion, it is unnecessary to postulate a perfect fluid because the effect of viscosity is nil.

1.7. Liquids and Gases. A fluid may be either a gas or a liquid. A gas completely fills the region within given boundaries regardless of the amount of gas enclosed, while a definite amount of liquid is required to fill a given region. A smaller amount of liquid will fill only part of the region, a free surface being formed as one boundary. In the words of Sir Oliver Lodge: "A solid has volume and shape, a liquid has volume but no shape, a gas has neither."

The most important difference between a liquid and a gas, from the viewpoint of fluid mechanics, is the fact that a liquid, like a solid, is practically incompressible under ordinary conditions, while a gas can be readily compressed. When the change in density of a gas is small, however, it can often be treated as an incompressible fluid to a good approximation.

A vapor is a gas that condenses to a liquid under lowered temperature or increased pressure. The pressure at which vapor begins to condense at any given temperature is called the "vapor pressure" or "saturation pressure." This pressure forms a limit below which laws applicable to gases cannot be used. Strictly speaking, all gases are vapors, since they can be condensed under extreme conditions. Vapors, however, behave like true gases under conditions sufficiently far removed from the saturation pressure.

In this study of fluid mechanics the treatment will ordinarily be restricted to practically incompressible fluids, with consideration given to compressibility only in special cases.

1.8. Concepts. The behavior of fluids is extremely difficult to describe or to observe in detail because there are no separate elements to be seen. In the mechanics of solid bodies we deal with separate entities of known dimensions and motions. A fluid, however, is continuous throughout a space, though its motion may be different at every point. Pressure, density, and temperature may vary throughout the space. Sometimes the flow seems to be regular, as if in layers, or laminae, and at other times it is confused and turbulent. Under some conditions large whirls or eddies occur.

Analysis is hopeless unless we can distinguish the conditions that are associated with the various types of behavior. Our method will be first to observe characteristic situations and then to devise simple idealized conditions that give an approximation of what has been observed. This method leads to a further classification, not as to the properties of the fluid itself, but rather as to the conditions under which the fluid is acting. Certain concepts will be required to define these conditions.

1.9. Continuity. The most conspicuous feature of fluids is that they generally exist and move as a continuous body of substance without voids. We postulate for analysis continuous flow such that at no place is fluid created or destroyed. We, in effect, affirm conservation of matter. Furthermore, we observe that in general, as in a river, the velocity, pressure, temperature, and density vary continuously from point to point at a given instant of time but at a given point may vary with time if the flow is not steady.

1.10. Continuum. This observation leads to the idealized conception of a continuum in which the quantities characterizing the flow, such as velocity, pressure, and density, are continuous functions of time and position. It then remains to consider under what conditions such a continuum represents our experience and also what meaning to attach to such ideas as pressure, density, and velocity at a point. When we examine these questions later, we shall conclude that gas in a vacuum tube contains too few molecules to be treated as a continuum. We shall see also that, under some conditions of flow, velocity is not a continuous function of position but may change suddenly at a so-called "surface of discontinuity" which separates, for example, a jet of air from the surrounding atmosphere.

1.11. Statics. We may greatly simplify our analysis if we first confine our attention to fluid at rest. It is common knowledge that liquids come to equilibrium with less dense fluid on top. We also know that the barometric pressure on a mountain peak is less than in a valley and that a deep-sea diver is subjected to greater pressure as he goes deeper. Furthermore, the phenomenon of convection, due to heating lower layers of fluid, is a rupture of a previous condition of stable equilibrium. From the principles of statics we can explain why a ship floats, why balloons rise in the air, and why other phenomena concerned with the stability of fluid at rest occur as they do.

1.12. Dynamics. Since flowing fluid is subjected to dynamic forces due to the motion, the distribution of pressure and density in the continuum, as determined by static conditions, can be greatly modified by the motion. By the principle of the conservation of energy we can predict the interchanges between kinetic and potential energy as a flow proceeds, and by means of a special form of Newton's second law of motion we can predict the dynamic forces exerted by the fluid.

In the mechanics of solids Newton's second law relates the force on a body of known mass to the rate of change in its momentum. In fluid mechanics individual masses are not distinguishable, and it is necessary to deal with a portion of the continuum contained within imaginary fixed boundaries. The resultant external force exerted on the fluid that at any instant lies inside this fixed "control volume" equals the rate of change of momentum of this fluid. Under certain conditions this force simply equals the difference between the rates of outflow and inflow of momentum across the boundary of the control volume.

1.13. Compressible and Incompressible Gases. We may simplify both the static and the dynamic problems of fluid mechanics by the assumption of constant density throughout the continuum. This is exactly what has been done in hydraulics, which deals exclusively with liquids. We know from experience that liquids are practically incompressible. Only when we deal with pressure waves in a liquid are we concerned with its compressibility.

Gases, however, are easily compressed, and substantial volume changes are produced in various types of machinery. For moderate changes in level the atmosphere behaves like an incompressible fluid, and appreciable density change requires an increase in altitude of the order of a mile. Likewise, for ordinary velocities (less than 250 mph) the density change produced by the motion is only a small fraction of the normal density. For velocities approaching the speed of sound (about 750 mph) compressibility is very important.

The facts of experience, therefore, tell us that liquids and atmospheric air may be treated as incompressible fluids in many practical cases. Air need be treated as a compressible fluid only where great density changes are brought about, as by great change in height, by machinery, or by extreme velocity.

For any object moving through a fluid there is some place on its surface where the relative velocity of the fluid is substantially higher than the velocity of translation. Consequently it is possible for this local velocity to reach the velocity of sound while the translatory velocity is subsonic.

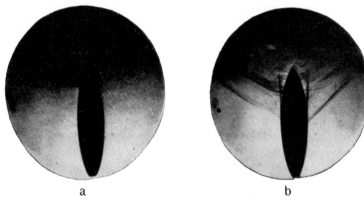

a   b

Fig. 1.3. — a. Flow past an airfoil at a speed well below that of sound. b. Flow in which sound velocity is reached locally in a region below the slanting dark lines (shock waves). The flow is upward in both pictures.

The velocity of translation at which local sonic velocity is encountered determines a critical speed for the particular shape of body, marked by the presence of standing compression waves.

Figure 1.3a is a photograph of the upward flow of air past an airfoil at a speed of 0.422 sound velocity. Figure 1.3b shows the flow pattern for the critical air speed at 0.776 sound velocity. The photographic method used makes visible variations in air density. In Fig. 1.3a the airflow is relatively smooth, and no marked discontinuity of density can be observed except close to the tail, where the flow separates to form a turbulent wake. At critical speed, Fig. 1.3b shows a great change. The dark lines across the airflow indicate regions of rapid change in density. Behind these lines the flow separates from the airfoil, and a broad wake is formed. The critical speed is marked by a large and abrupt increase in resistance.

The difference in the flow for the two photographs is a consequence of compressibility. At critical speed the airflow next to the thickest part of the model has reached the speed at which a pressure wave is propagated. Hence, pressure changes on the rear of the model cannot influence the flow over the forward part since a pressure change cannot be propagated upstream. To preserve equilibrium a discontinuity of pressure (and density) occurs in the form of standing waves, or "compression shocks," shown by the dark lines. The very sharp increase in pressure at the compression shocks forces the flow to separate from the model, leaving a broad wake. In general, a critical flow is unsteady, and the position of the compression shocks fluctuates with time.

The technical measure of high speed is the Mach number M, defined as the ratio of the general flow velocity to the velocity of sound in the fluid. Subsonic velocity is indicated by $M < 1$ and supersonic velocity by $M > 1$. Airplanes fly at subsonic velocity but may reach a critical speed in a dive with consequent serious effects on control and structural integrity. Propellers, superchargers, and other machinery frequently handle air at critical speeds and higher. Bombs dropped from a great height may attain and pass through a critical velocity. Projectiles are fired with an initial supersonic velocity.

In the discussion of the dynamics of fluid motion, compressibility cannot be neglected when the Mach number approaches unity.

1.14. Steady Motion. The simplest case of flow is a steady motion whose pattern is the same at all times. Such a flow is seen in the steady jet from a nozzle, the steady current in a river, or the steady wind at a good height above the ground. Mathematically we express this statement that the velocity field is independent of time and depends only on the space coordinates x, y, z thus:

$$V = f(x,y,z)$$

Steady motion may be incompressible or not, depending on whether the density is constant or a function of location.

1.15. Boundary Layer. When one looks over the side of a vessel proceeding in smooth water, a belt of so-called "friction eddies" is seen, made visible by day because of air released and often by night by phosphorescence in the water. Just outside this belt the flow seems to be steady and of the order of the velocity of the ship. Since the water wets the ship and is carried along with it, there is, close to the ship's hull, a high velocity gradient that makes viscosity important and creates a strong frictional drag on the hull (see Fig. 1.4).

Outside the boundary layer the velocity gradients are small; hence, for this steady motion, friction or viscosity should be unimportant. The fluid outside the boundary layer seems to flow in a steady and frictionless manner.

Accordingly, to approximate the complicated motion of real fluids, it has been found generally useful to consider the continuum as made up of two distinct and separate portions, the boundary layer and wake, where friction controls the motion, and the region outside, where friction can be neglected. The justification for this concept, due to Prandtl, is its evident

resemblance to the observed state of affairs and the useful practical results
that can be obtained from analyses based on it.

Observation of real fluids shows no discontinuity in velocity through

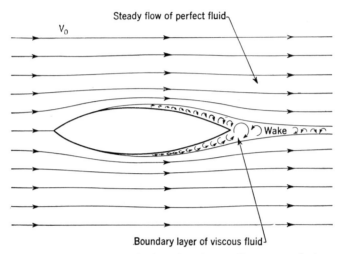

Fig. 1.4. — Fluid particles entering the boundary layer adjacent to a body are set into
rotation by the action of viscosity.

the boundary layer. Figure 1.5 indicates a rapid but smooth transition
of velocity from zero to V_0 in passing out from the ship's side through a
boundary layer such as is represented in Fig. 1.4.

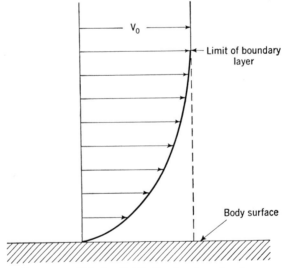

Fig. 1.5. — Velocity distribution in a boundary layer.

1.16. Discontinuity. Where a sharp corner projects into the flow, the steady stream of fluid would be thrown clear, as in Fig. 1.6a. On one side of DD there is dead water and on the other the full velocity of the stream. There is consequently a discontinuity of velocity, but not of fluid. The

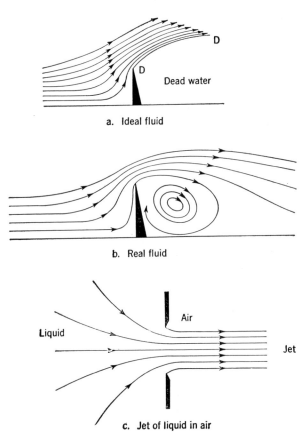

a. Ideal fluid

b. Real fluid

c. Jet of liquid in air

FIG. 1.6. — Surfaces of discontinuity in velocity.

velocity gradient is, for an ideal fluid, infinite at such a "surface of discontinuity."

For real fluids having friction the abrupt change in velocity (high velocity gradient) causes large frictional forces tangential to the direction of motion. The dead water is set into rotation by the stream. The eddy that builds up is indicated in Fig. 1.6b.

A liquid jet in air, as from a nozzle, is surrounded by a surface of discontinuity. Here the liquid continuum may be considered to extend throughout the tank and the jet but not to cross the surface of the jet into the air (see Fig. 1.6c).

Observed phenomena frequently show a distinct separation of the flow from the object about which it flows. Such separation appears to be associated with a rapid change in contour, which the fluid will not follow. Flow separation involves a surface of discontinuity that breaks up into eddies. The ideal concept of a continuum can represent only the region not containing a surface of discontinuity.

Flow separation is of great technical importance because smooth flow is destroyed and energy losses become very large. An airplane stalls when the flow separates from the wing flown at too high an angle of incidence.

1.17. Laminar and Turbulent Flow. Observation shows that fluid flowing very slowly through a pipe or flowing through a very small capillary tube moves steadily in parallel layers having different speeds. This kind of motion is called "laminar flow." The boundary layer on a smooth object in a free stream may likewise show laminar flow for low speeds.

In pipes of sufficient size and at sufficient velocity the flow breaks up into a confused turbulence. A similar transition from laminar to turbulent flow, depending on flow conditions, is observed generally in boundary layers.

It is helpful to classify any flow in the region of a boundary or in a pipe as either laminar or turbulent and to develop an analysis for each. Each is observed in nature and must be accounted for in any theory that pretends to predict natural phenomena.

1.18. Rotation. In the flow of real fluids it is observed that abrupt deflection of the flow by a solid object often gives rise to separation, followed by whirling eddies, or vortices. Parts of the fluid are evidently set into rotation of a peculiar sort, which persists for an appreciable time. A surface of discontinuity seems to be unstable and to roll up into a vortex. Another sort of rotation of fluid is an obvious feature of centrifugal pumps and hydraulic turbines.

We, therefore, must examine the nature of rotation in a fluid continuum. For this purpose a further classification of fluid phenomena will be discussed, *viz.*, irrotational and rotational flow, corresponding somewhat to the appearance of what is observed.

1.19. Circulation. When a solid body, submerged in a fluid stream, is placed in such an attitude as to deflect the stream, a force is created transverse to the stream. On an airplane wing this force is called a "lift"; on a propeller blade it is called a "thrust." Experiment has shown that the pressure on the surface of a deflector is higher than normal over the face and lower than normal over the back, evidently giving rise to the lifting force observed. There is also experimental evidence to indicate that the flow is speeded up along the back of the deflector and slowed down along the face. This observed speeding up and slowing down can be accounted for if we imagine an idealized case in which there is a circulation of fluid about the deflector which combines with the transverse flow to produce the velocity distribution observed in nature. This concept of circulation leads to a useful theory of lift applicable to machinery, making use of dynamic forces transverse to the general direction of fluid flow.

1.20. Density. Newton's second law states that the product of mass times acceleration equals the sum of all external forces acting on the body under consideration. To apply this statement to a fluid requires careful consideration of the concept of mass with special relation to a fluid continuum.

A fluid mass distributes itself throughout a continuum in such a manner that there are no voids; consequently, there is fluid at every point. We can consider the quotient obtained by dividing the mass Δm, within a small element of volume enclosing the point, by the volume ΔV of this element. The result is in terms of mass per unit volume and is called the "average density" of Δm.

It is a basic assumption of a fluid continuum (without voids) that every element of volume ΔV contains a definite mass of fluid Δm, and it follows that the density must have a definite value at every point. We define density at a point, therefore, as the limit of $\Delta m/\Delta V$ as $\Delta V \to 0$, or $\rho = dm/dV$.

Since a finite mass $m = \int dm$, it follows that $m = \int \rho\, dV$.

The density may vary in a continuous manner from point to point. If the fluid flow is unsteady, the density at a given point may also vary with time. In general, for the idealized continuum, density is a single-valued continuous function of time and position, or

$$\rho = \frac{dm}{dV} = f(x,y,z,t)$$

Density has no physical significance if ΔV, as it approaches zero, momentarily contains no molecules. We therefore restrict our concept of a continuum to apply to fluids in which there is a large number of molecules in any volume element which is small relative to the extent of fluid. Thus for air at atmospheric pressure a volume element of $1/10^9$ cu mm contains some 3×10^7 molecules.

Although molecular agitation causes molecules continually to pass in and out of a fixed element of volume, the average number contained in such an element will remain substantially constant and the fluid can be treated as a continuum with a definite density at every point. The concept of density at a point as a statistical quotient also applies to the analogous concept of temperature, which is measured by the mean value of the kinetic energy of the molecules per unit volume.

In a vacuum tube the mean free path of the molecules may be of the order of the size of the tube, and density at a point can have no meaning. The concept of a continuum does not apply to problems of high vacua.

In a real fluid, volume elements lose identity through interchange of molecules by diffusion, but the continuum approximates a state of affairs that exists for an appreciable period of time. The interchange of molecules between volume elements is also responsible for internal friction or viscosity (interchange of momentum between layers of fluid in relative motion) and for heat conduction (interchange of molecular kinetic energy).

In an ideal fluid continuum we ignore molecular agitation. Observed large-scale phenomena such as viscous shear and heat conduction are satisfactorily accounted for by assigning to the continuum the properties of viscosity and thermal conductivity, which vary continuously with position and time. We choose to overlook the molecular origin of these properties.

1.21. Pressure. In fluid mechanics not only density, but also pressure, has special significance and requires precise definition. It is obvious that any portion of a fluid must experience a force acting on it due to the surrounding fluid. If this were not the case, a portion of the fluid could move under the influence of gravity and there would be no state of rest or equilibrium. We must, therefore, accept the compulsory hypothesis of external forces proportional to the surface area. There will also be body forces proportional to the mass of the element of volume in consideration, *e.g.*, its weight.

In addition to external surface and body forces there will be internal forces within any volume element; but, as is the case for solid bodies, the internal forces mutually cancel.

As the element of volume is imagined to contract toward zero, the body forces, which are proportional to volume and hence to the third power of a linear dimension, become negligible with respect to the surface forces, which are proportional to the surface and hence to the square of a linear dimension.

Consequently, we have left for consideration only the external surface forces, which must be in equilibrium among themselves for a sufficiently small portion of a fluid.

For an ideal fluid without friction the surface force on an element of fluid must be perpendicular to the surface on which it acts. For a real fluid at rest the surface force is also perpendicular since, when there is no motion, there is no friction. This conclusion applies only to a true fluid whose viscosity is defined by the Newtonian relation between force and rate of deformation.

We now examine the meaning of "pressure at a point" in a fluid at rest in the light of the two conclusions that the surface forces on a sufficiently small element of volume are in equilibrium and are perpendicular to the surfaces on which they act.

Pressure is defined as stress, or surface force per unit area,

$$p = \lim_{\Delta A \to 0} \frac{\Delta F}{\Delta A} = \frac{dF}{dA}$$

Since we may choose a volume element of any form, consider a small prism as shown in Fig. 1.7 near a point O in a fluid at rest. We choose the volume so small that body forces can be neglected; hence the element to be in equilibrium must have no resultant horizontal or vertical surface force acting on it.

Hence,

$$p_3 \, dy \, dz = p_2 \, dy \sqrt{dx^2 + dz^2} \sin \alpha$$

and

$$p_1 \, dy \, dx = p_2 \, dy \sqrt{dx^2 + dz^2} \cos \alpha$$

But

$$\cos \alpha = \frac{dx}{\sqrt{dx^2 + dz^2}}$$

and

$$\sin \alpha = \frac{dz}{\sqrt{dx^2 + dz^2}}$$

Therefore

$$p_3 = p_2 = p_1$$

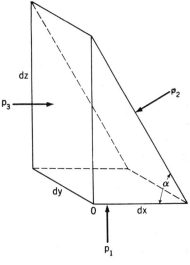

FIG. 1.7.

Since the volume element may be chosen with any orientation and since we may make the element as small as we please, we may say that the pressure p at or near the point O is independent of the orientation of the surface element on which it acts. The name "hydrostatic pressure" is given to p, a scalar quantity expressed as force per unit area.

We may consequently define p as a continuous function of position.

$$p = f(x,y,z)$$

This statement is true for all fluids at rest. For a viscous fluid in motion there is friction, and the force on a surface element near any point depends on the orientation of the surface element with respect to the motion. Therefore, to describe the stress distribution at a point, we need a sphere for a fluid at rest, and an ellipsoid for a viscous fluid in motion, identical with the ellipsoid of stress for a solid. For an ideal fluid the pressure at a point is independent of the direction of the surface element on which it acts, regardless of whether the fluid is at rest or in motion.

1.22. Concluding Remarks. The foregoing discussion is intended as a general survey of the problem of fluid flow. It is to be noted that the problem can have many aspects, each characterized by a concept peculiar to a recognizable type of flow. These concepts are justified only to the extent that they lead to useful approximations.

Historically, the science of fluid mechanics stems from Archimedes, who understood statics. Euler developed the concept of the ideal fluid continuum and the dynamic equations of motion. He may fairly be credited with establishing the dynamics of ideal fluids, or the science of hydromechanics, which was notably extended in the nineteenth century by the theoretical work of Helmholtz, Kirchhoff, Kelvin, Lamb, and Rayleigh. However, it was not until after the stimulation given experimental research by aeronautics, in the present century, that the behavior of real fluids began to be understood. To one man more than to any other, L. Prandtl of Göttingen, belongs the credit for illuminating the facts of observation by application of the general principles of mechanics.

Three fundamental concepts, defining simplifying assumptions, mark the renaissance of nineteenth-century classical hydromechanics into the practical fluid mechanics of today. The first is the concept of the boundary layer surrounded by an ideal continuum, due to Prandtl. The second, independently proposed by Lanchester and Kutta and later developed into useful form by Joukowski and Prandtl, is the circulation theory, by means of which forces on wings and propeller blades may be predicted. A third concept, of great practical utility, is the theory of dimensions, which we shall discuss in connection with experimental work. Though dimensional theory was not new to physics, Lord Rayleigh showed how it could be used to generalize the results of empirical but controlled model experiments to yield information needed for the design of airplanes, ships, machinery, and many other engineering applications of fluid mechanics. Where the actual flow is too complex for theoretical analysis, tests with a scale model can often guide the designer to a practical solution of his problem.

CHAPTER II

STATICS

The equilibrium and stability of a fluid at rest will be developed from the fundamental concept of a fluid continuum in which the pressure at any point has a single positive value $p = f(x,y,z)$. The fluid may be viscous, but if so it must be of so-called "Newtonian" character. The statement regarding pressure could also be made regarding the density at any point $\rho = f(x,y,z)$, since pressure and density are related by a simple physical law, the equation of state. The concept of mass will be required in the discussion of dynamics of a fluid, but it is not essential to statics. We are, however, directly concerned with the weight of the fluid since weight is the primary cause of hydrostatic pressure.

Under what conditions does a fluid remain in equilibrium? We define equilibrium as a state in which each particle or portion is at rest or has no velocity with respect to a suitable system of reference. Consequently, there can be no relative motion between adjacent portions of the fluid. As a suitable system of reference for practical problems of engineering we can use a system either rigidly connected to the earth or having a uniform translation with respect to the earth. In either case the fluid under consideration has no acceleration with respect to the earth. The absence of acceleration is identical with the condition that the sum of forces is zero. Thus we can say that equilibrium is a state in which the resulting force on each portion of the fluid is zero.

There are two kinds of force to be considered, one due to gravity, the other due to the interaction between neighboring particles, the hydrostatic pressure. There are no frictional or tangential forces in the absence of relative motion between portions of the fluid.

2.1. Gravity Force. Gravity acts toward the center of the earth, but in engineering problems we can assume that all gravity forces are parallel. The magnitude of the gravity force, or weight, acting on an element of volume dV is $\gamma\, dV$, where γ, the weight per unit volume, or specific weight, is equal to ρg, the product of density times the acceleration g. There are few cases in engineering in which the decrease of g at high altitudes is important.

2.2. Pressure Force. The problem in the theory of equilibrium of fluids is to find an expression for the resulting force on the surface of an element of volume dV due to the surrounding fluid. Consider an element of cylindrical shape (Fig. 2.1). The cross section of the small cylinder is dA, and its length is dx. The orientation of the cylinder is arbitrary, so that we may choose as its direction that of our x axis. The volume of the

15

element $dV = dA\ dx$. There are three groups of pressure forces acting on the cylinder, (1) the pressure forces acting on the convex surface, which have different directions but which are all perpendicular to the x axis; (2) the pressure force on the left-hand base, which has the x direction; and (3) the pressure force on the right-hand base, which has the opposite, or the minus, x direction. If we confine ourselves to the x component of the resulting force, we may disregard forces 1 and consider only the difference between force 2 and force 3. If p is the pressure at the center of the left-

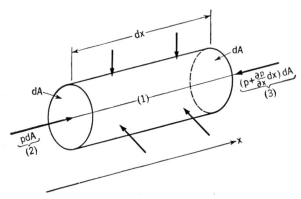

Fig. 2.1.

hand base, we can say that $p\ dA$ is the magnitude of force 2. We really assume that p may be treated as constant over an infinitesimal area.

The pressure at the center of the right-hand base will in general be different from p. Let us call this pressure $p + dp$. But since p is a function of the location of a point in the fluid, or of x, y, z, the notation dp by itself is not clear. The change in p is not the same for each direction when we proceed from a given point. What we need to know is the change in p that corresponds to proceeding a distance dx along the x direction. It is usual to denote the rate of increase of a variable p by $\partial p/\partial x$ when the point in consideration is moved in the x direction. ($\partial p/\partial x$ = partial derivative of p with respect to x.) Therefore our dp, which measures the increase of p from one point to a neighboring one on the x axis, is written $(\partial p/\partial x)\ dx$. It follows that the resulting force in the x direction is given by

$$p\ dA - \left(p + \frac{\partial p}{\partial x}\ dx\right) dA = -\frac{\partial p}{\partial x}\ dx\ dA \qquad (2.1)$$

If we divide this expression by the volume $dV = dx\ dA$, we obtain the resulting pressure force in the x direction per unit of volume

$$-\frac{\partial p}{\partial x}\frac{dx\ dA}{dV} = -\frac{\partial p}{\partial x} \qquad (2.2)$$

The x component of the resultant of all pressure forces acting upon an infinitely small element has, per unit of volume, the value $-\partial p/\partial x$, that is, the negative partial derivative of p with respect to x.

The expression "x direction" is used here quite arbitrarily; we could replace it by any other, such as y direction or z direction. In each case the component of the resulting pressure force per unit of volume is determined by the negative partial derivative of p in the corresponding direction. If we use the ordinary rectangular coordinate system with x, y, and z axes, calling K_x, K_y, K_z the resulting pressure forces per unit of volume in the x, y, and z directions, we have

$$\left.\begin{aligned} K_x &= -\frac{\partial p}{\partial x}\\[2pt] K_y &= -\frac{\partial p}{\partial y}\\[2pt] K_z &= -\frac{\partial p}{\partial z} \end{aligned}\right\}\qquad(2.3)$$

In vector analysis, the gradient of a scalar function is the vector whose components parallel to the three axes are the partial derivatives of the function with respect to the three coordinates x, y, z. Gradient means rate of increase. We may concisely state that the *resulting pressure force per unit of volume is the negative gradient of p* where p is considered a function of x, y, and z. Note that the hydrostatic pressure p at any point is a scalar quantity without direction, while the resulting force per unit volume due to hydrostatic pressure is a vector having a definite direction determined by the gradient of p.

Consider, for example, a pressure distribution that is a linear function of x, y, z: $p = ax + by + cz$. Here the partial derivatives of p are $\partial p/\partial x = a$, $\partial p/\partial y = b$, $\partial p/\partial z = c$. The resulting pressure force per unit of volume has therefore the constant value $\sqrt{a^2 + b^2 + c^2}$, and its direction is determined by the constant ratios $a/b/c$. The pressure is constant in each plane the equation of which is given by $ax + by + cz =$ constant. The normal to this plane is again given by the ratio $a/b/c$. According to the well-known formulas of analytic geometry these are the ratios of the three direction cosines, $\cos\alpha/\cos\beta/\cos\gamma$. The same direction is the direction of the force vector whose components are a, b, and c. From this example we can make the general statement that the resulting pressure force is perpendicular to the surface on which p has a constant value. Such surfaces are called "isobars," and the resulting pressure force is normal to the isobar passing through a point and is directed toward the isobars with smaller pressure values [because of the minus sign in Eq. (2.3)].

All this becomes clearer if we consider the special case in which the constants a and b are zero and p is simply equal to cz. Then $\partial p/\partial x = 0$,

$\partial p/\partial y = 0$, and $\partial p/\partial z = c$. The xy planes are the isobars, or surfaces of constant pressure. The resultant pressure force, or the gradient of p, is parallel to the z axis since its x and y components are zero. If the positive z direction is assumed to be upward, the z component of the resultant force is directed vertically downward for a positive value of c, and vice versa.

In the present discussion it does not matter whether the fluid is compressible or incompressible. In either case the resultant pressure force per unit of volume at any point has the components $-\partial p/\partial x$, $-\partial p/\partial y$, $-\partial p/\partial z$.

2.3. Conditions of Equilibrium. When the expression for the resultant pressure force is known, there is no difficulty in setting up the conditions of equilibrium for a fluid. As was mentioned before, the only forces acting on a fluid particle are due to gravity and hydrostatic pressure. The gravity force per unit volume (or specific weight) has the magnitude γ and is directed vertically downward. The pressure force per unit volume has the components $-\partial p/\partial x$, $-\partial p/\partial y$, $-\partial p/\partial z$, and its direction at any point is normal to the isobar passing through the point and is directed toward decreasing values of p. In a coordinate system of arbitrary orientation the components of the weight per unit volume may be called γ_x, γ_y, γ_z, and the equilibrium conditions at any point, x, y, z, will be

$$\left. \begin{aligned} \gamma_x - \frac{\partial p}{\partial x} &= 0 \\[2mm] \gamma_y - \frac{\partial p}{\partial y} &= 0 \\[2mm] \gamma_z - \frac{\partial p}{\partial z} &= 0 \end{aligned} \right\} \tag{2.4}$$

Usually it will be convenient to use a coordinate system where the z axis is vertical and the positive z direction is upward. In this case gravity has no x or y components, and its z component is negative.

$$\gamma_x = 0 \qquad \gamma_y = 0 \qquad \gamma_z = -\gamma \tag{2.5}$$

With respect to such a coordinate system the three equilibrium conditions simplify to

$$\frac{\partial p}{\partial x} = 0 \qquad \frac{\partial p}{\partial y} = 0 \qquad \frac{\partial p}{\partial z} = -\gamma \tag{2.6}$$

or, in words: A fluid mass is in equilibrium if the isobars are horizontal planes and if the pressure increases downward at the rate γ. The fact that $\partial p/\partial x$ and $\partial p/\partial y$ are zero means that p is a function of z alone. It follows that $\partial p/\partial z$ can be written in the form dp/dz in this case. The pressure gradient dp/dz, or the resultant pressure force per unit of volume, has, therefore, a constant value in each horizontal plane.

We draw an important conclusion from the fact that dp/dz is constant for each horizontal plane. Since Eq. (2.6) shows that $- dp/dz = \gamma$, the specific weight and consequently the density ρ must be constant in a horizontal plane if the fluid is in equilibrium. (We assume that variations in $g = \gamma/\rho$ are negligible.) This statement is of course of no interest for an incompressible fluid, where density has the same value everywhere, but it is important for gases or other compressible fluids. For this latter case we have established the fact that a fluid mass can be in equilibrium only if the density is constant along horizontal isobars. A mixture of insoluble liquids at rest becomes stratified with lighter liquid on top.

If we took the spherical shape of the earth into account, the isobars would be concentric spheres with centers at the center of the earth. In the case of a compressible fluid like the atmosphere, the density would be constant over all such spherical surfaces if the fluid mass were in perfect equilibrium.

When the vertical distance z alone appears in the equations of equilibrium, we do not need a three-coordinate system. We shall use the letter h (height) instead of z to denote the vertical distance of a point above an arbitrarily chosen level.

We can now summarize the conditions for static equilibrium in the following three statements:

1. Pressure is constant in each horizontal plane.
2. Pressure decreases upward at the rate γ, or

$$\frac{dp}{dh} = - \gamma \tag{2.7}$$

3. In the case of compressible fluids, density is constant in each horizontal plane.

Note that in the theory of static equilibrium there is no difference between ideal and viscous fluids. The three above-stated equilibrium conditions are valid for both cases.

2.4. Potential. It will later be necessary in the discussion of dynamics to introduce a potential function to facilitate the analysis. For statics the concept of potential in a gravity field is especially simple owing to its identity with potential energy.

For a fluid at rest under gravity, the weight per unit volume is $\gamma = g\rho$, acting downward. The acceleration of gravity is a vector of constant magnitude, and unit mass of fluid has the same weight g regardless of position.

Define a potential function P of h such that

$$\frac{dP}{dh} = - g$$

Therefore

$$P = -g \int_{h_0}^{h} dh = -g(h - h_0)$$

where h and h_0 are heights above some arbitrary datum level and the value of P at h_0 has been arbitrarily taken as zero. Note that, for a given elevation, P is constant and that the gradient of P in the direction of h gives the gravity force $-g$ in the same direction. Define potential energy per unit mass at height h with respect to height h_0 as the work done in lifting unit mass from h_0 to h,

$$E_1 = -g(h - h_0)$$

Since E_1 and P are identical, we can state that the numerical value of the potential function at any level is equal to the potential energy of unit mass of fluid at that level.

The kinetic energy of unit mass after falling freely a distance $h - h_0$ has the same numerical value,

$$E_2 = \tfrac{1}{2}(V^2) = \tfrac{1}{2}[\sqrt{2g(h - h_0)}]^2 = g(h - h_0)$$

2.5. Equilibrium of Incompressible Fluids (Hydrostatics). Water, oil, and similar liquids can be considered as incompressible and the density as constant throughout the continuum. Under this condition the basic

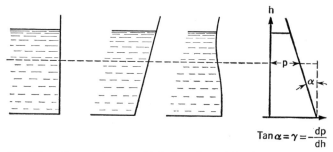

$$\text{Tan}\,\alpha = \gamma = -\frac{dp}{dh}$$

Fig. 2.2. — Pressure in a vessel is independent of the shape of the wall.

equation of equilibrium, Eq. (2.7), can easily be integrated. From $dp/dh = -\gamma$ follows

$$p + \gamma h = \text{constant} \quad \text{or} \quad \frac{p}{\gamma} + h = \text{constant} \tag{2.8}$$

Pressure is evidently a linear function of h, increasing downward at a rate γ. The pressure diagram that has h as a vertical coordinate consists, therefore, of an oblique straight line as shown in Fig. 2.2.

Along the side wall of a vessel filled with liquid the pressure increases from its value at the top to its value at the bottom according to the linear law as shown. The shape of the wall has no influence on the pressure at a given level.

The lighter the fluid, the smaller the angle α between the oblique straight line and the vertical.

In the ordinary problems of hydrostatics, we shall often have as reference level the free surface of the liquid exposed to the atmosphere. The vertical pressure gradient of the atmosphere is $dp/dh = -\gamma_a$, where γ_a is the specific weight of air. Since the density of air is very small compared with the density of liquids, we shall be justified in neglecting it. Therefore, within a restricted region we can assume a constant atmospheric pressure p_0, regardless of elevation of the liquid surface.

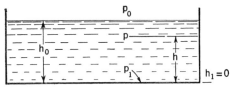

FIG. 2.3.

Where the liquid touches the atmosphere, the pressure in the liquid must equal the atmospheric pressure p_0. It follows that the boundary between liquid and atmosphere is an isobar $p = p_0$; and since all isobars are horizontal planes, we have proved the well-known fact that the free surface of a liquid in equilibrium is a horizontal plane.

Two exceptions may be mentioned. (1) In problems involving very large dimensions, such as an expanse of ocean, the free surface will be a spherical one with the center at the center of the earth, and the isobars will be spherical surfaces. (2) In certain problems involving very small dimensions additional molecular forces exerted on the liquid particles by a wall must be considered.

The general condition of equilibrium for incompressible fluids as given in Eq. (2.8) can also be written in the form

$$p + \gamma h = p_1 + \gamma h_1 = p_0 + \gamma h_0 \qquad (2.9)$$

where the pairs p, h; p_1, h_1; and p_0, h_0 refer to three different levels in the fluid. We may take, as in the case of Fig. 2.3, the bottom of the tank as the level of reference, calling this level 1. Then the height h_0, which is equal to the depth of the water, refers to the top where the pressure p_0 is the atmospheric pressure. At an arbitrary height h or at a depth $h_0 - h$ the pressure is p, and Eq. (2.9) shows that

$$p + \gamma h = p_1 = p_0 + \gamma h_0$$

or

$$p - p_0 = \gamma(h_0 - h) \quad \text{and} \quad p_1 - p_0 = \gamma h_0 \qquad (2.10)$$

The last equation can be read as follows: The pressure increase from the surface to any point within the fluid equals the product of γ times its depth below the free surface. It is convenient in many cases to use as the measure of pressure the pressure difference $p - p_0$, that is, the absolute pressure minus the atmospheric pressure. This difference is often called the "gauge" pressure, or overpressure.

Let us now consider the second form of the equilibrium equation as given in Eq. (2.8)

$$\frac{p}{\gamma} + h = \text{constant}$$

The quotient p/γ should have the dimensions of a length; otherwise it could not be a term summed up with h. But it is evident that, since p has

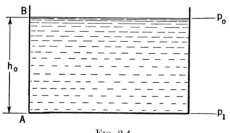

the dimensions force/length^2 and γ the dimensions force/length^3, p/γ has the dimension of length. This length p/γ has an immediate physical significance, which can be illustrated by an example.

Consider a vertical column of fluid from A to B (Fig. 2.4), where B is a free surface. Then

Fig. 2.4.

$p_1 - p_0 = \gamma h_0$, where h_0 is the length AB. It follows that

$$AB = h_0 = \frac{p_1 - p_0}{\gamma}$$

We see that, if $p_1 - p_0$ is the gauge pressure at the bottom of the column, then the height of the column is $(p_1 - p_0)/\gamma$. In this way pressure values can be visualized by lengths, *i.e.*, heights of columns with a free surface and a certain pressure value at the bottom. In hydraulics it is usual to call the quotient p/γ the pressure head corresponding to p.

2.6. Some Applications of the Hydrostatic Equation. *a. Communicating Vessels.* The pressure in a fluid is a function of height only, and at the

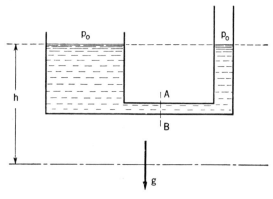

Fig. 2.5.

free surfaces is equal to the general atmospheric pressure. Therefore, the free surfaces in all communicating vessels are at the same height.

It has been mentioned that the equilibrium conditions within a fluid mass are in no way altered by the shape of the vessel which contains the fluid. As long as the fluid forms a continuum, the equation $p + \gamma h =$ constant applies to all its parts. If the vessel in Fig. 2.5 is filled with a liquid,

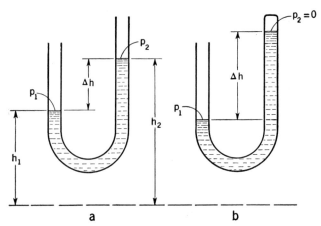

FIG. 2.6. — *a.* Manometer. *b.* Barometer.

the level of the free surface in each leg is the same. Also, the pressure p in any horizontal plane is the same in each leg. Nothing could be said about the levels and pressures if the fluid were separated by a wall along the line AB.

b. Barometer and Liquid Manometer. Referring to Fig. 2.6 we see that, in the manometer, at h_1,

$$p = p_1$$

while at h_2,

$$p = p_2$$
$$p_1 - p_2 = \gamma \, \Delta h$$

In the barometer,

$$p_1 = p_0$$
$$p_2 = 0, \text{ approximately}$$
$$p_1 - p_2 = p_0 = \gamma \, \Delta h$$

In the barometer, p_2 is nearly zero if the instrument is carefully filled with mercury initially. The right-hand leg is open, so that there the atmospheric pressure p_0 acts on the mercury. If γ_{Hg} designates the specific weight of mercury (848 lb per cu ft) and p_0 the atmospheric pressure, the equilibrium condition yields the equation

$$p_0 = \gamma_{Hg} \, \Delta h$$

Since γ_{Hg} is known, the reading of the distance Δh indicates the atmospheric pressure. The pressure of the atmosphere is often expressed in terms of pressure head of mercury. The usual average value for sea level is 760 mm, or 29.92 in., Hg.

c. Hydraulic Press. A well-known application of the laws of hydrostatics is made in the hydraulic press, as shown in Fig. 2.7. In order to exert a large force F on the piston of area A, it is sufficient to produce the

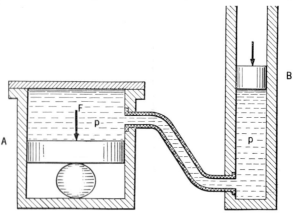

Fig. 2.7. — Hydraulic press.

pressure $p = F/A$ above the piston. This can be done according to the law of communicating vessels by producing the same pressure p in the smaller cylinder of area B, which requires only the force $pB = FB/A$. The small differences in height are neglected here, and so are friction and inertia forces, as we assume very slow motion of the pistons. If the body underneath the piston A has its height reduced by ϵ, the work done is $F\epsilon = pA\epsilon$. This movement requires a transition of a volume of liquid $A\epsilon$ from the small cylinder to the large one. It follows that the small piston B must move a distance $\epsilon_1 = \epsilon A/B$. The work done by the piston B is $pB\epsilon_1 = pB\epsilon A/B = pA\epsilon$, equal to the work done by the large piston in compressing the body below it. The small piston has the greater motion, but a small force on B can balance a large force on A.

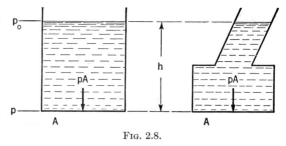

Fig. 2.8.

d. Pressure on Floors; Hydrostatic Paradox. Since the pressure p_0 at the free surface is the same for both vessels of Fig. 2.8, the pressures at the same depth in

gravity is independent of the density of the fluid and depends only on the geometry.

h. Convection. Suppose a chimney of height h discharges smoke and warm air into the atmosphere at pressure p_c corresponding to the level of the chimney top of Fig. 2.11. Let the pressure in the fireplace be p_f and the pressure in the air outside be p_0. Assume the average specific weight of the warm gases in the chimney to be γ_c and that of the cool air outside to be γ_a. The warm gas is lighter, and $\gamma_a > \gamma_c$. Neglecting any acceleration of the air, we find by the hydrostatic equation

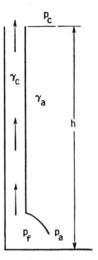

$$p_f - p_c = \gamma_c h \qquad p_0 - p_c = \gamma_a h$$

and

$$p_0 - p_f = h(\gamma_a - \gamma_c)$$

This approximate analysis, based on the assumption of equilibrium, shows that the two columns of equal height are actually not in equilibrium and air will flow into the fireplace. A rising column of fluid caused by unequal heating is called a "convection current." It is not necessary to have a fireplace and chimney to start convection. Any local heating of a portion of fluid in a

FIG. 2.11.

continuum will destroy the previously established condition of equilibrium. The convective currents tend to establish a new state of equilibrium. Convection in the atmosphere due to unequal heating of the surface of the ground may be very marked over a region with adjoining areas of bare ground, forest, and lakes. On a clear summer day an airplane's flight may be very rough although no evidence of disturbance of the air is visible.

2.7. Pressure Measurement. If we wish to know the pressure at any point P in a liquid, we attach a tube as shown in Fig. 2.12. This tube may be filled with any liquid that does not mix with and that has a

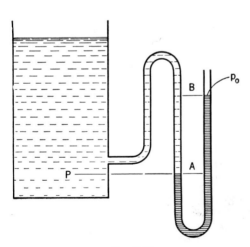

FIG. 2.12.

greater density than the liquid in the vessel. We must take care that the liquid in the tube is in equilibrium. Then the distance AB between the

each are equal provided that both are filled with fluid of the same density. Hence if the areas of the bottoms A are equal, the total force pA is the same on the bottom of each vessel in spite of the obvious difference in the total weights of liquid contained.

e. Pressure on Walls. Let h be the distance, or "head," measured down-

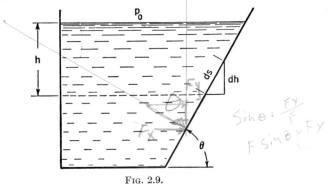

FIG. 2.9.

ward from the free surface of Fig. 2.9. Then, at depth h, $p = p_0 + \gamma h$, and the normal force per unit width of a vertical wall,

$$F = \int_0^h (p_0 + \gamma h)\, dh$$

The normal force per unit width of a sloping wall,

$$F_s = \int_0^{h/\sin\theta} (p_0 + \gamma h)\, ds = \int_0^h (p_0 + \gamma h)\, \frac{dh}{\sin\theta} = \frac{F}{\sin\theta}$$

when θ is constant.

The horizontal component of the force on the sloping wall is $F = F_s \sin\theta$. In general, the horizontal component of the total force due to hydrostatic pressure on a wall of any slope or shape is equal to that on a vertical wall of the same depth.

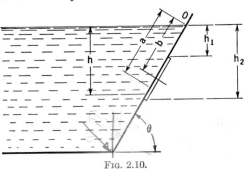

FIG. 2.10.

f. Force on an Area. We first compute the total hydrostatic force on the water gate in the sloping dam shown in Fig. 2.10.

$$\text{Area of gate} = A = \int_{h_1}^{h_2} dA$$

$$\text{Force on gate} = F = \int_{h_1}^{h_2} (p - p_0) \, dA = \gamma \int_{h_1}^{h_2} h \, dA$$

Let b be the distance measured along the face of the dam to the center of gravity of the area of the gate. The moment of the area A about O is

$$Ab = \frac{1}{\sin \theta} \int_{h_1}^{h_2} h \, dA = \frac{1}{\sin \theta} \frac{F}{\gamma}$$

and

$$F = A\gamma b \sin \theta$$

But the pressure at the center of gravity of A is

$$p_c = \gamma b \sin \theta$$

Therefore,

$$F = A p_c$$

The general rule follows that the total force due to hydrostatic pressure on an inclined plane surface is equal to the area of the surface times the pressure at its center of gravity. This force is independent of the inclination of the surface.

g. Center of Pressure. Referring again to Fig. 2.10, we ask for the point on the gate of area A through which passes the line of action of the force F. Call this point the center of pressure, and let it be a distance a from O. The moment of F about O is Fa.

The pressure at the center of an element of area dA is γh, and the normal force on the element is $\gamma h \, dA$. The moment of this force about O will be $\gamma h \, dA(h/\sin \theta)$, and the moment of all such forces will be the sum, or integral, of such elementary moments.

Then, taking the moment of F about O and remembering that F is normal to the gate, we find

$$Fa = \int_{h_1}^{h_2} \gamma h \, dA \, \frac{h}{\sin \theta} = \int_{h_1}^{h_2} \gamma \, dA \left(\frac{h}{\sin \theta}\right)^2 \sin \theta$$

$$= \gamma I \sin \theta$$

where I is the moment of inertia of A about O. But $F = \gamma b \sin \theta \, A$; and, by substitution for F in the above equation,

$$a = \frac{I}{bA} = \frac{\text{moment of inertia about } O}{\text{moment of area about } O}$$

If I_g is the moment of inertia of the gate about its center of gravity, $I = I_g + b^2 A$ and $a - b = I_g/bA$, which is always positive. The center of pressure, therefore, lies below the center of gravity.

Note that the location of the center of pressure relative to the center of